CW00429362

Title - A Change of Heart
ISBN 13 - 978-1-955144-08-7
Composer - Andrew T Hanna
Graphic Design, Layout, & Artwork - Andrew T Hanna

Genre - Jazz, Jazz-Fusion, Jazz-Rock, Progressive

Score

A Change of Heart

Andrew Hanna

7
D♭-Δ7
E♭07
A♭Δ7
A. Sax.
Bass
Dr.
9
F-Δ7
G07
C-7
A. Sax.
Bass
Dr.
11
Double Time
A. Sax.
Bass
Dr.
15
A♭Δ7
D♭-Δ7
E♭07
A. Sax.
Bass
Dr.

18
B♭-Δ7
A♭Δ7
D♭Δ7
A. Sax.
Bass
Dr.
21
G♭Δ7
E♭7
al fine
A. Sax.
Bass
Dr.

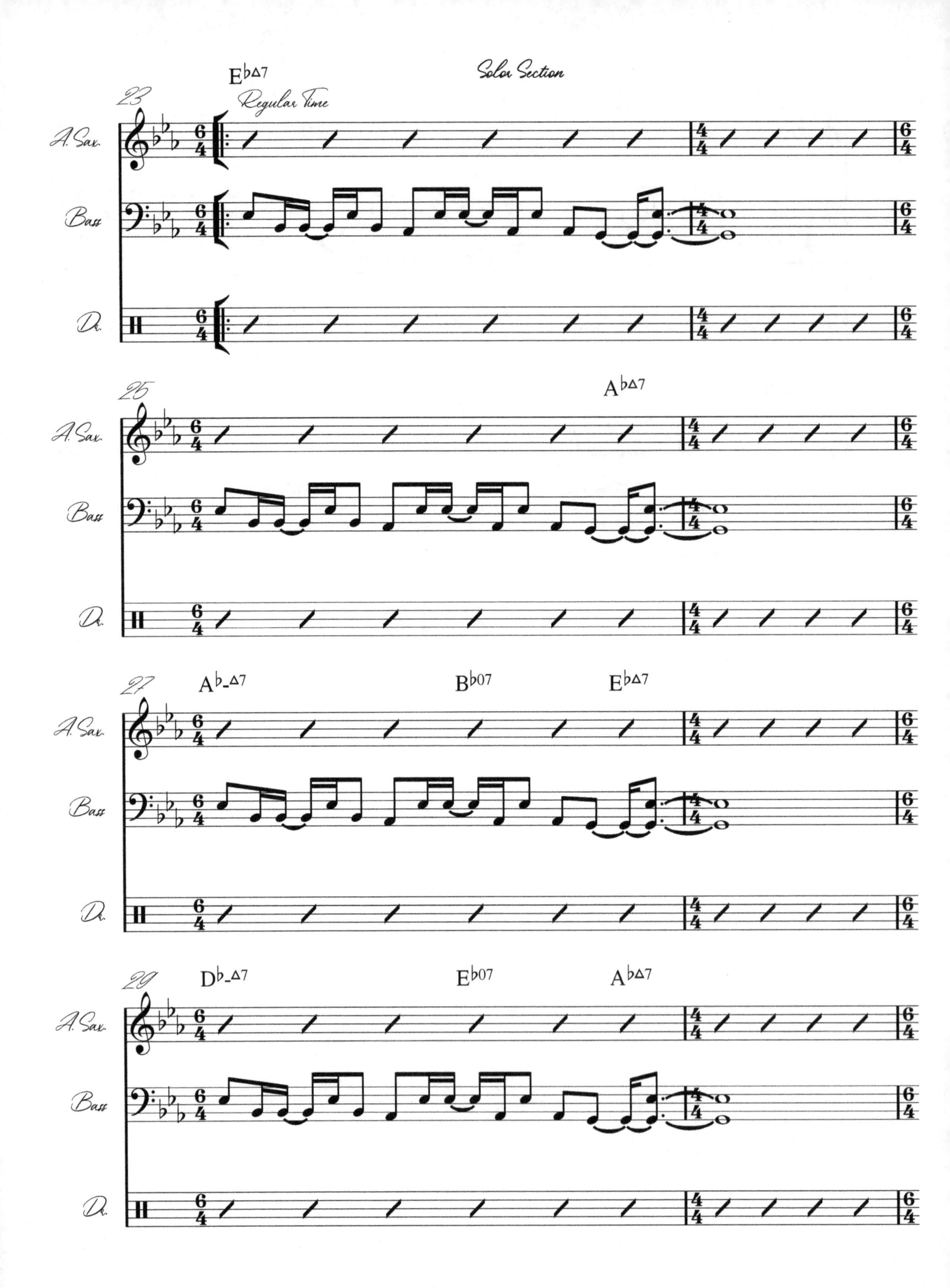

Solos Section
23
E♭Δ7
Regular Time
A. Sax.
Bass
Dr.
25
A♭Δ7
27
A♭-Δ7
B♭07
E♭Δ7
29
D♭-Δ7
E♭07
A♭Δ7

31
F-Δ7
G07
C-7
A. Sax.
Bass
Dr.
33
Double Time
37
A♭Δ7
D♭-Δ7
E♭07
40
B♭-Δ7
A♭Δ7
D♭Δ7

43
G♭Δ7
E♭7
D.C. al fine
A. Sax.
Bass
Dr.

Alto Sax

A Change of Heart

Alto Sax

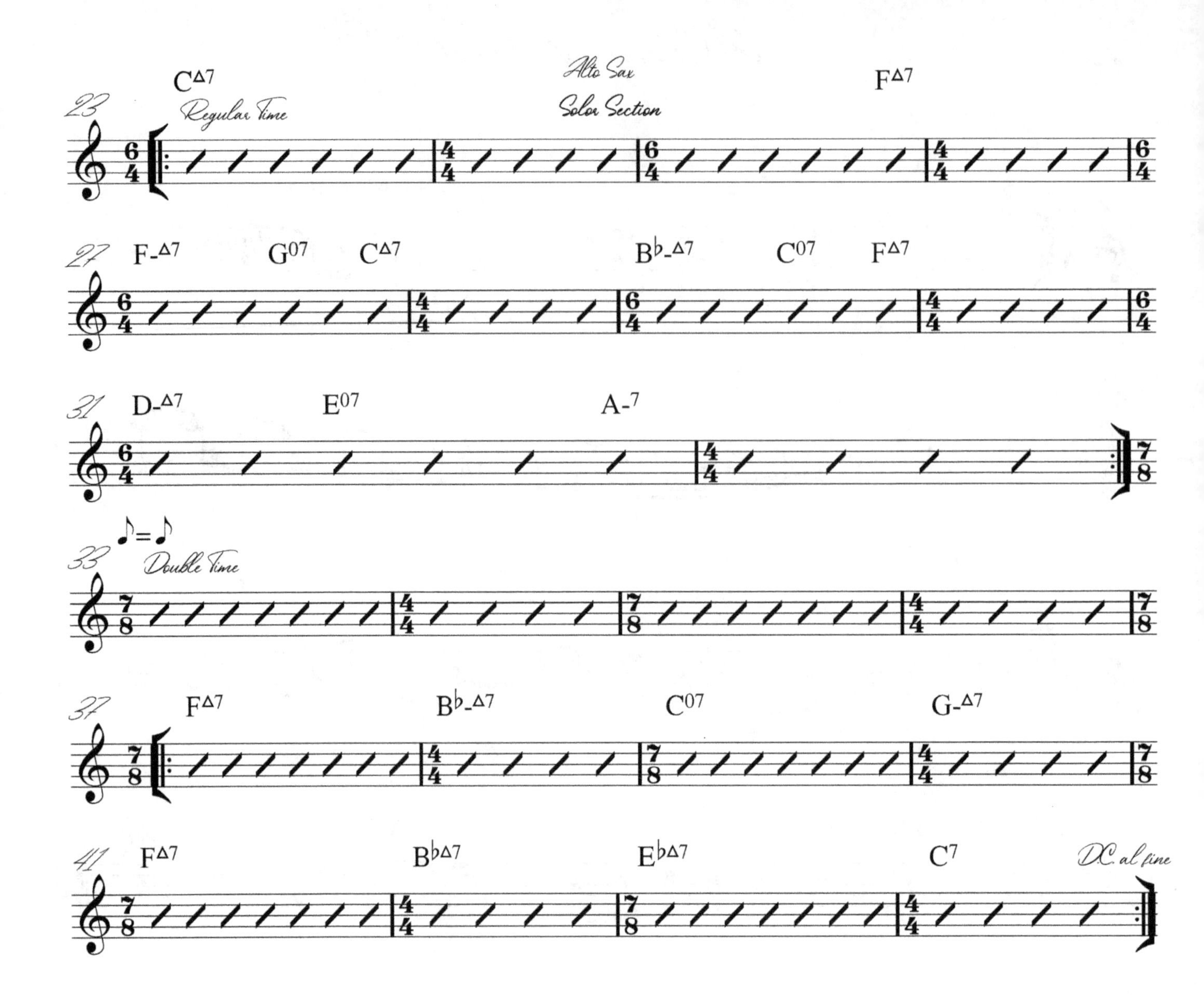
Alto Sax
Solos Section
23
C∆7
Regular Time
F∆7
27
F-∆7
G07
C∆7
B♭-∆7
C07
F∆7
31
D-∆7
E07
A-7
33
Double Time
37
F∆7
B♭-∆7
C07
G-∆7
41
F∆7
B♭∆7
E♭∆7
C7
D.C. al fine

Bass Guitar

A Change of Heart

Bass

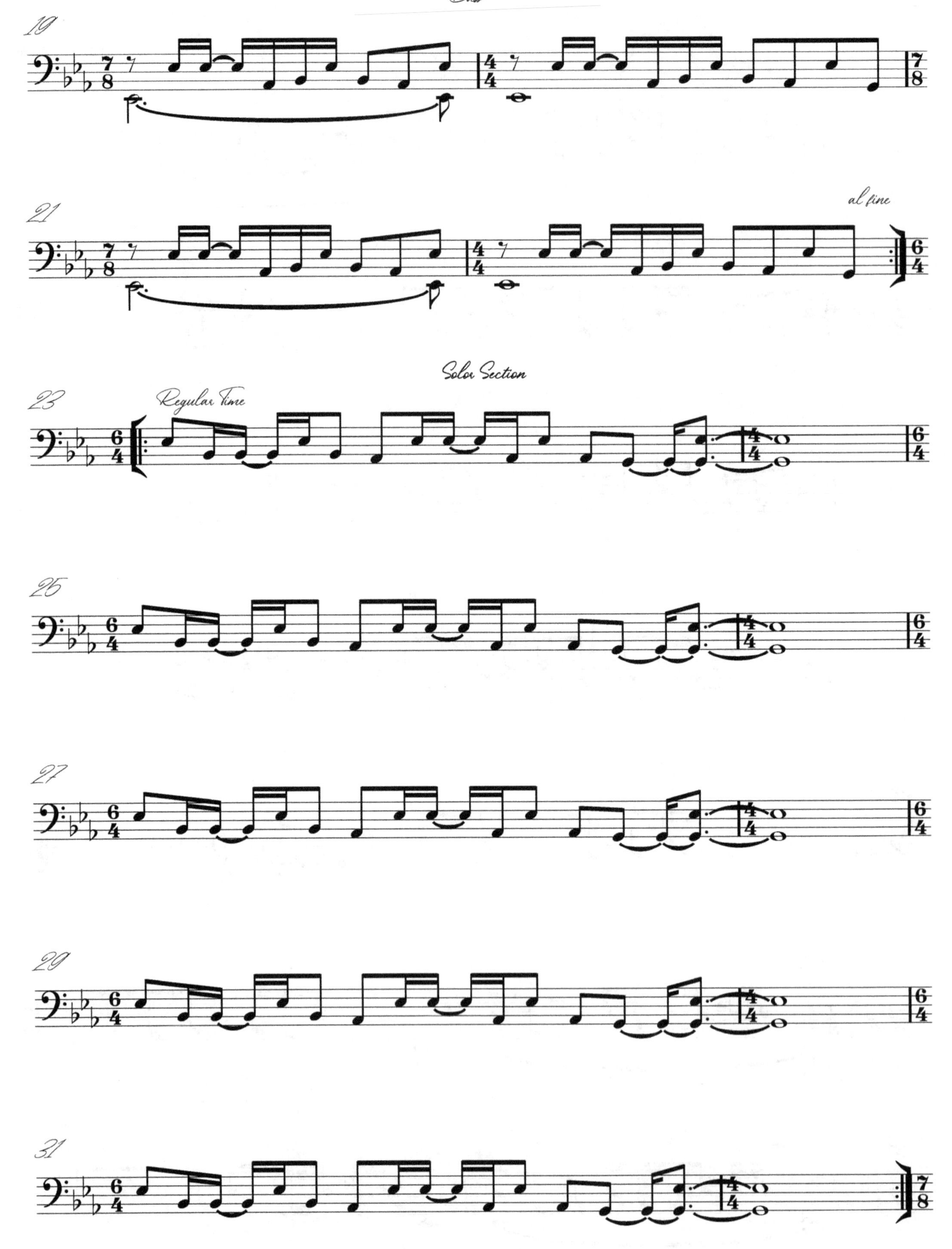
Bass
19
21
al fine
Solos Section
23
Regular Time
25
27
29
31

Bass
Double Time
33
35
37
39
41
43
D.C. al fine

Drum Set

A Change of Heart

Drum Set

Andrew Hanna

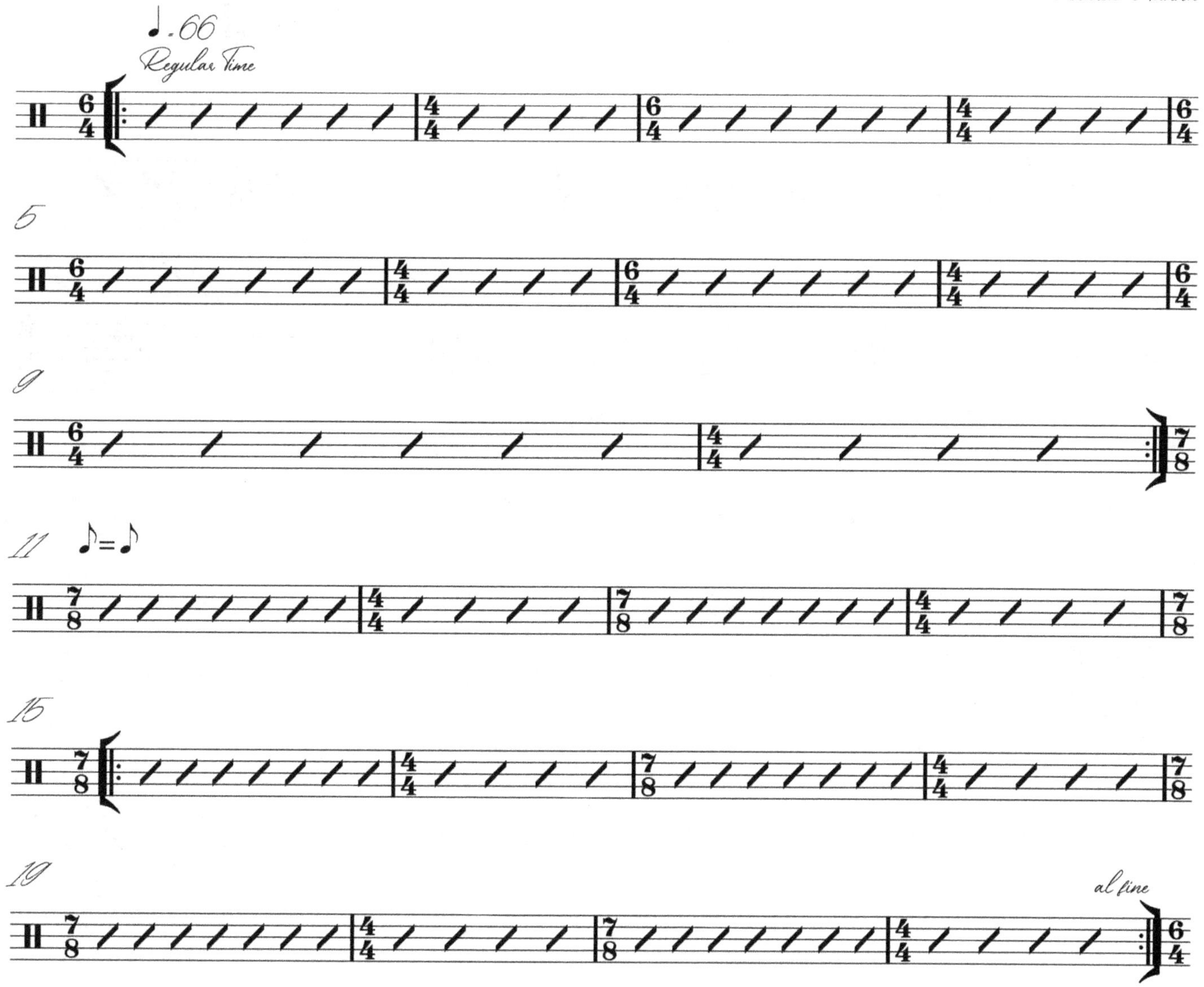

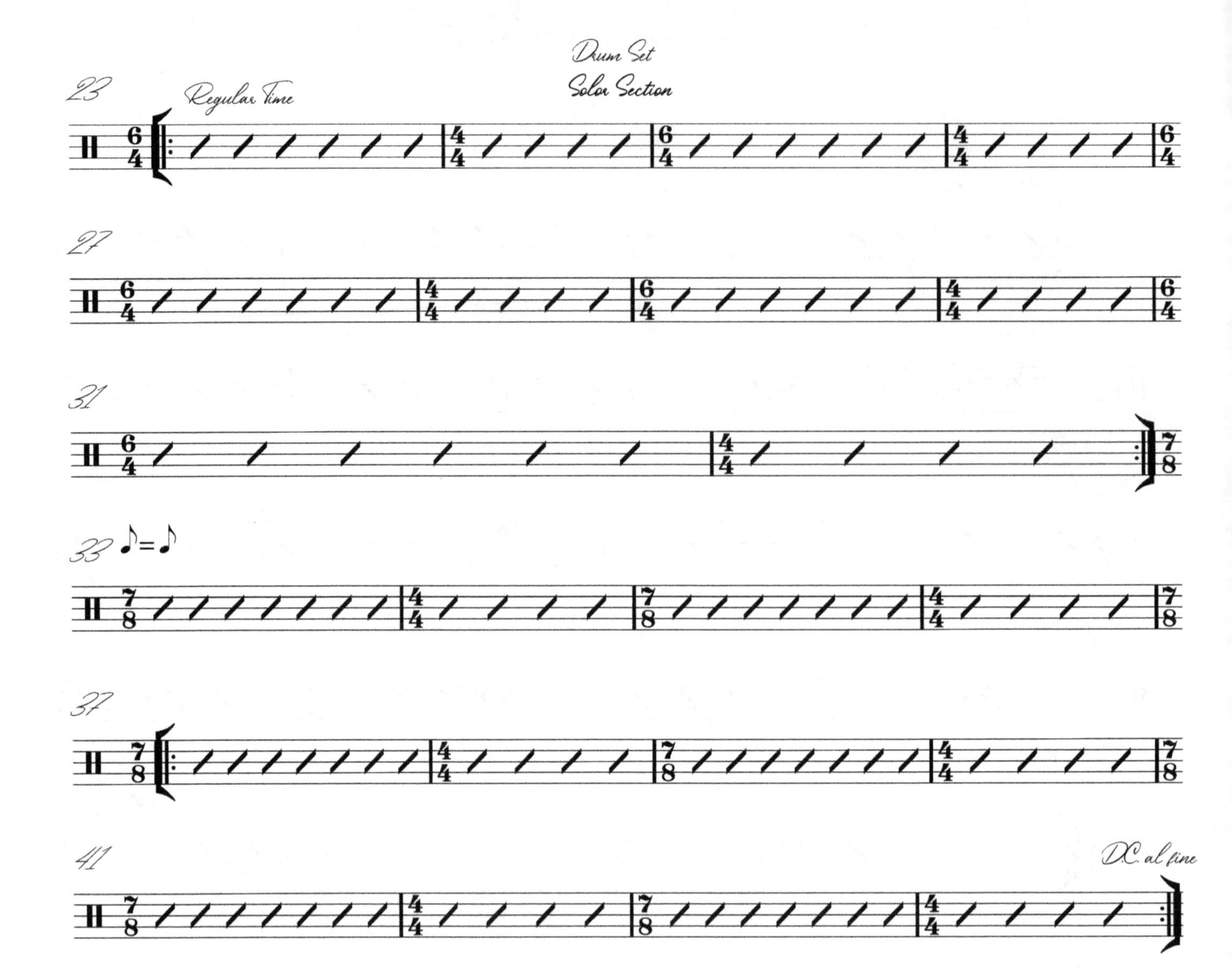
Drum Set
Solor Section
23
Regular Time
27
31
33
37
41
D.C. al fine

CPSIA information can be obtained
at www.ICGtesting.com
Printed in the USA
LVHW061308181022
730903LV00013B/445